ANIMAL RHYTHMS
VOWELS

By Cindy McCord and Shirley Ross

Publisher: Roberta Suid
Editor: Mary McClellan
Design and production: Susan Cronin-Paris
Art: Susan Cronin-Paris and Shirley Ross
Cover Design: David Hale

ISBN 0-912107-71-5

Printed in the United States of America
9 8 7 6 5 4 3 2 1

INTRODUCTION

Animal Rhythms is a reading program designed to help young children associate the letters of the alphabet with their sounds. Each letter has an animal whose name begins with that letter's sound: Alligator Ann teaches the short sound of "a"; and Uni Unicorn, the long "u" sound. Accompanying each letter-animal friend is an alliterative chant called the animal rhythm, which reinforces the letter sound as the children memorize it and repeat it over and over.

In *Animal Rhythms–Vowels,* each animal has a section of activities all its own, with worksheets with similar formats for all sections.

Worksheets

• Introducing the Letter Animal

The first worksheet in each section introduces the animal, the letter, and the sound it represents. The children learn the animal's name and color the things in the picture that begin with the same letter sound. They recite the alliterative animal rhythm, listening to the sound of the letter at the beginning of each word. The letter's uppercase and lowercase forms are included on the page for the children to trace over and over with several colors from their crayon boxes. This is called "rainbow writing."

• Visual Discrimination

The second worksheet for each short vowel sound shows an object that begins with that sound. The object is filled with an assortment of alphabet letters, most of which are the one being taught. The children circle all of the appropriate letters. At the bottom of the page, there are letters for the children to trace.

• Auditory Discrimination

The next worksheet provides auditory discrimination practice. The children cut and paste the appropriate pictured objects around the animal friend. There are some things on the page which do not begin with the sound studied. The uppercase and lowercase forms of the letter are pictured on the page. This is another opportunity for the children to trace the letters over and over with many different colors from their crayon boxes.

• Short and Long Vowel Sound Discrimination

The short and long vowel sounds are compared and reviewed using cut-and-paste activities. The two animal friends for each letter are pictured on the page, with spaces in which the students paste pictures that have been cut from the bottom of the page.

Activities

• Make-a-Word Books

The Make-a-Word Books give the children practice with word families, where the short vowel is used in the middle of one-syllable words. There are two books for each vowel sound. The animal friend is pictured in a rectangle at the top of the page. The four sections under the picture contain an outline of a square and a letter form. The section at the bottom is longer than the middle three and has the word ending.

The children make these pages into a book. The cover is the section with the animal's picture on it. The last page is the word family section. Give the children pictures of objects whose names belong to the appropriate word family. Instruct them to color the pictures, cut them out on the dotted lines, and paste them in their books in the square on the correct page.

• Take-Home Activities

The first Take-Home Activities provide auditory discrimination practice. After each short vowel sound is studied, give the students copies of the animal and the corresponding page of pictures. Have them color the animal friend and cut it into two parts, cutting carefully on the dotted line. After the children have cut out the pictures, they can play the game by naming the pictures and placing the ones that have the appropriate vowel sound in a row between the two parts of the animal. Alligator Ann will grow longer and longer. Elephant Ed's trunk gets bigger, while Ichabod Indri climbs higher in his tree. Oliver Ostrich's neck stretches as each short "o" object is named, and Umbrella Bird's tail feathers grow.

The second Take-Home Activities provide visual discrimination practice. The heads and word wheels should be put together using brads. The children can play the game by moving the wheel and then saying the word shown.

Name _____

Color Alligator Ann and the things that begin with the short sound of a. Trace the Aa's with lots of colors. Listen to the sound of a as you chant Ann's animal rhythm.

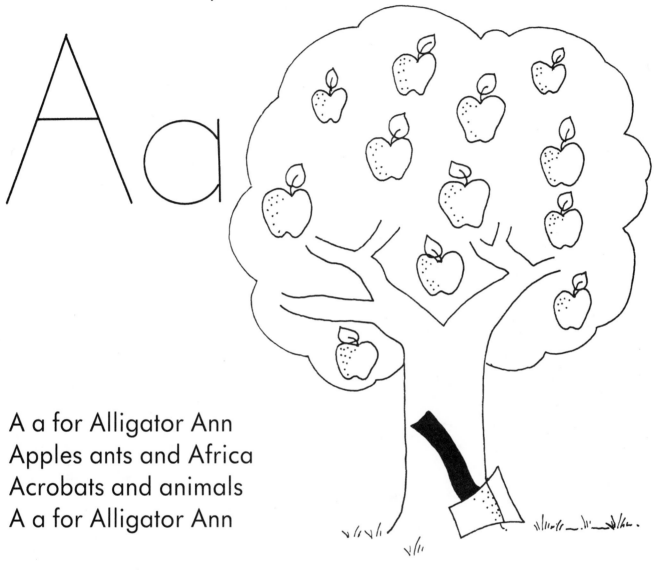

A a for Alligator Ann
Apples ants and Africa
Acrobats and animals
A a for Alligator Ann

Name _____

Find the Aa's on Alligator Ann's apples. Circle each one. Trace the Aa's.

Name _____

Cut out the pictures that begin with the short sound of a. Paste them by Alligator Ann. Trace the Aa's with lots of colors.

Color Elephant Ed and the things that begin with the short sound of e. Trace the Ee's with lots of colors. Listen to the sound of e as you chant Ed's animal rhythm.

E e for Elephant Ed
Every extra energy
Empty echoes exercise
E e for Elephant Ed

Name _____

Find the Ee's on Elephant Ed's eggs. Circle each one. Trace the Ee's.

Name _____

Cut out the things that begin with the short sound of e. Paste them by Elephant Ed. Trace the Ee's with lots of colors.

© 1988 Monday Morning Books, Inc.

Name _____

Color Ichabod Indri and the things that begin with the short sound of i. Trace the Ii's with lots of colors. Listen to the sound of i as you chant Ichabod's animal rhythm.

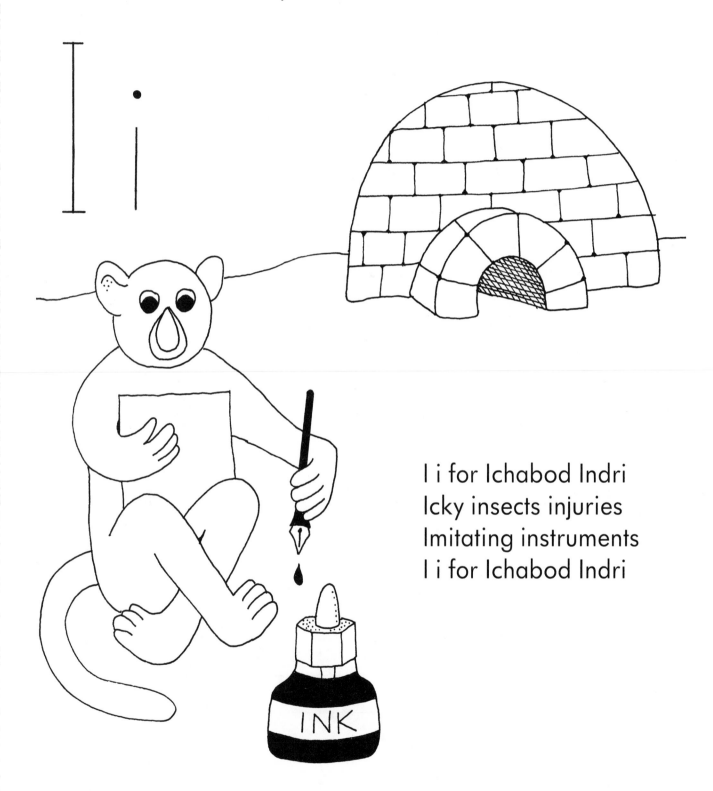

I i for Ichabod Indri
Icky insects injuries
Imitating instruments
I i for Ichabod Indri

Name _____

Find the Ii's on Ichabod Indri's igloo. Circle each one. Trace the Ii's.

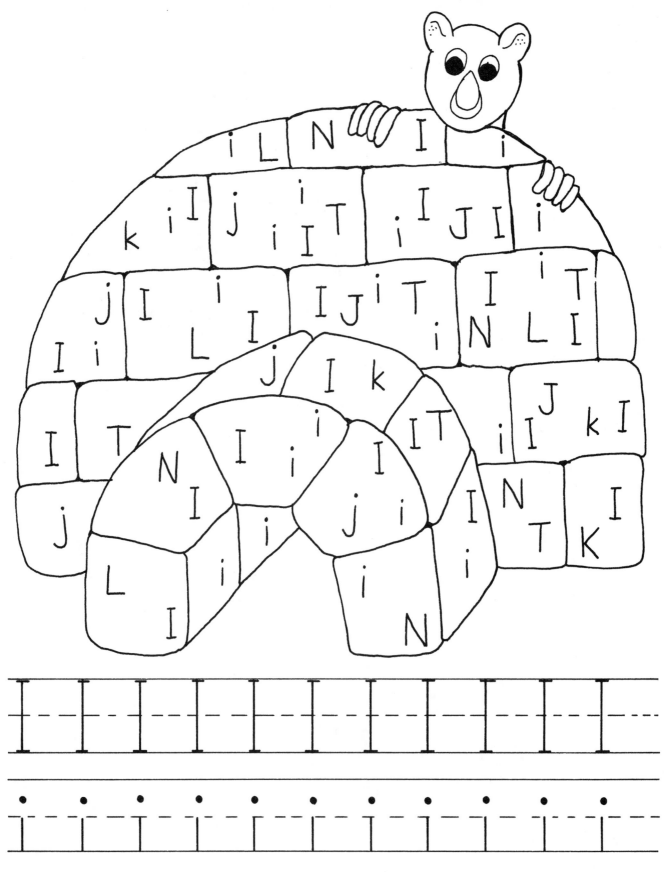

Name _____

Cut out the pictures that begin with the short sound of i. Paste them by Ichabod Indri. Trace the Ii's with lots of colors.

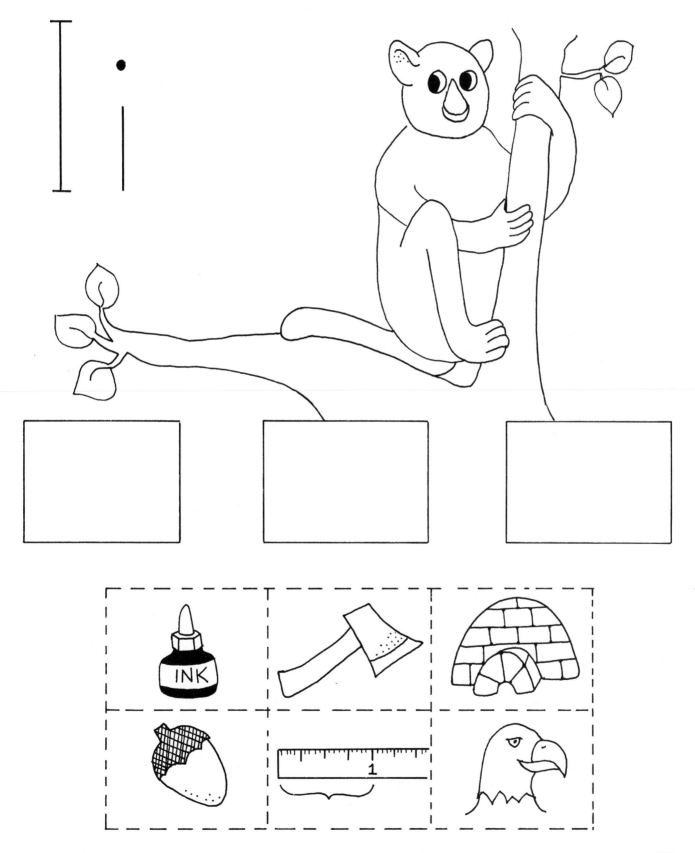

13

Name _____

Color Oliver Ostrich and the things that begin with the short sound of o. Trace the Oo's with lots of colors. Listen to the sound of o as you chant Oliver's animal rhythm.

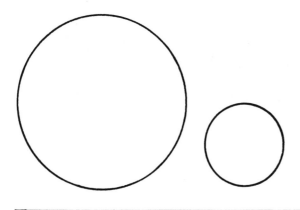

O o for Oliver Ostrich
Octopus and operate
Oblong olives off and on
O o for Oliver Ostrich

Name _____

Find the Oo's on Oliver Ostrich's olives. Circle each one. Trace the Oo's.

Name _____

Cut out the pictures that begin with the short sound of o. Paste them by Oliver Ostrich. Trace the Oo's with lots of colors.

Name _____

Color Umbrella Bird and the things that begin with the short sound of u. Trace the Uu's with lots of colors. Listen to the sound of u as you chant Umbrella Bird's animal rhythm.

U u for Umbrella Bird
Upset uncle's underwear
Up and under ugliness
U u for Umbrella Bird

Name _____

Find the Uu's on Umbrella Bird's umbrella. Circle each one. Trace the Uu's.

Name _____

Cut out the things that begin with the short sound of u. Paste them by Umbrella Bird. Trace the Uu's with lots of colors.

Color Amy Ape and the things that begin with the long sound of a. Trace the Aa's with lots of colors. Listen to the sound of a as you chant Amy's animal rhythm.

A a for Amy Ape
Able angels aliens
Aprons acorns ancient age
A a for Amy Ape

Name _____

Cut out the pictures that begin with the long sound of a. Paste them by Amy Ape. Trace the Aa's with lots of colors.

Color Egret Eve and the things that begin with the long sound of e.
Trace the Ee's with lots of colors. Listen to the sound of e as you
chant Eve's animal rhythm.

E e for Egret Eve
Eating eels eagerly
Easy Easter evenings
E e for Egret Eve

Name _____

Cut out the pictures that begin with the long sound of e. Paste them by Egret Eve. Trace the Ee's with lots of colors.

Name _____

Color Ibex Ike and the things that begin with the long sound of i. Trace the Ii's with lots of colors. Listen to the sound of i as you chant Ike's animal rhythm.

I i

I i for Ibex Ike
Icy iron icicles
Irish ivy iodine
I i for Ibex Ike

Name _____

Cut out the pictures that begin with the long sound of i. Paste them by Ibex Ike. Trace the Ii's with lots of colors.

Name _____

Color Olivia Opossum and the things that begin with the long sound
of o. Trace the Oo's with lots of colors. Listen to the sound of o as
you chant Olivia's animal rhythm.

O o for Opossum
Only open overalls
Over oceans oval oats
O o for Opossum

Name _____

Cut out the pictures that begin with the long sound of o. Paste them by Olivia Opossum. Trace the Oo's with lots of colors.

27

Color Uni Unicorn and the things that begin with the long sound of u. Trace the Uu's with lots of colors. Listen to the sound of u as you chant Uni's animal rhythm.

U u for Unicorn
Using useful utensils
Unicycle uniform
U u for Unicorn

Name _____

Cut out the things that begin with the long sound of u. Paste them by
Uni Unicorn. Trace the Uu's with lots of colors.

Name _____

Cut out the things that begin with the short sound of a. Paste them by
Alligator Ann. Cut out the things that begin with the long sound of a.
Paste them by Amy Ape.

Name _____

Cut out the things that begin with the short sound of e. Paste them by Elephant Ed. Cut out the things that begin with the long sound of e. Paste them by Egret Eve.

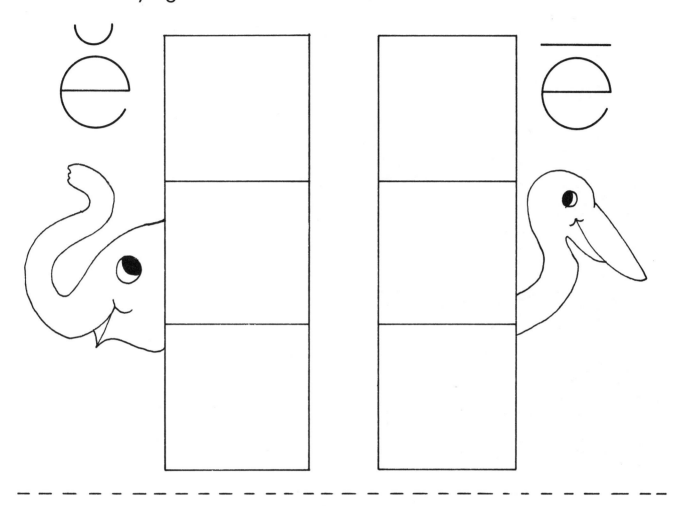

Name _____

Cut out the things that begin with the short sound of i. Paste them by
Ichabod Indri. Cut out the things that begin with the long sound of i.
Paste them by Ibex Ike.

Name _____

Cut out the things that begin with the short sound of o. Paste them by Oliver Ostrich. Cut out the things that begin with the long sound of o. Paste them by Olivia Opossum.

Name _____

Cut out the things that begin with the short sound of u. Paste them by Umbrella Bird. Cut out the things that begin with the long sound of u. Paste them by Uni Unicorn.

Make a Word Book

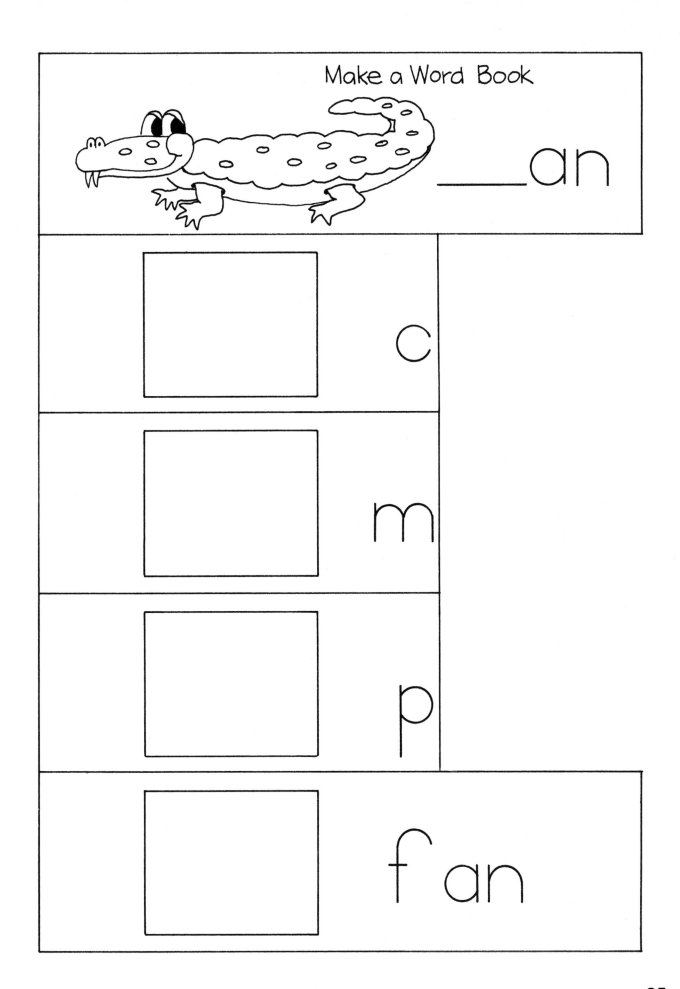

___an

c

m

p

f an

Make a Word Book

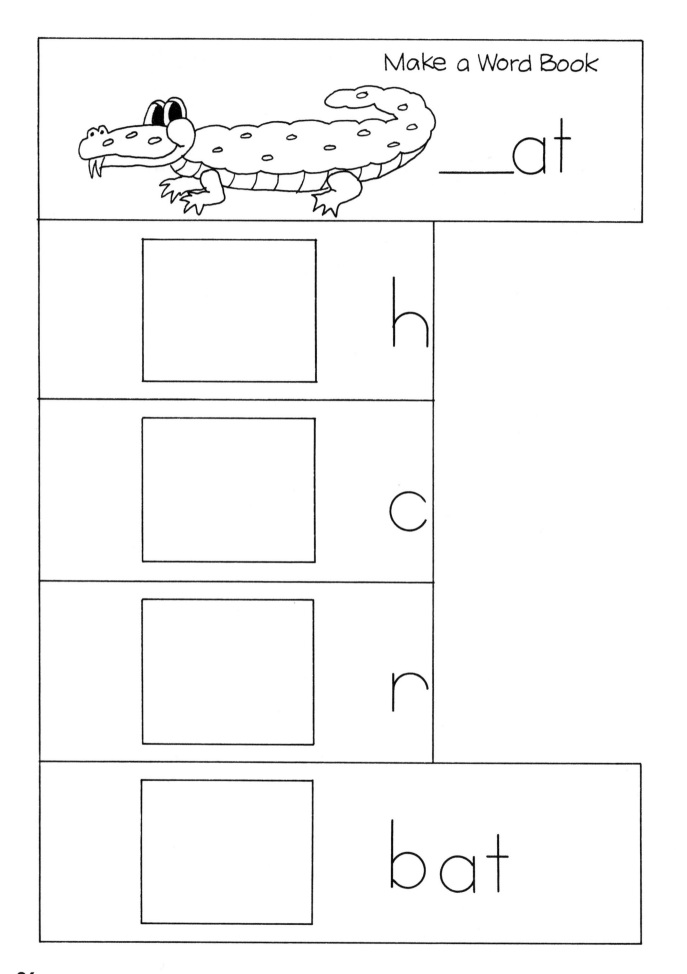

___at

h

c

r

b a t

an

at

Make a Word Book

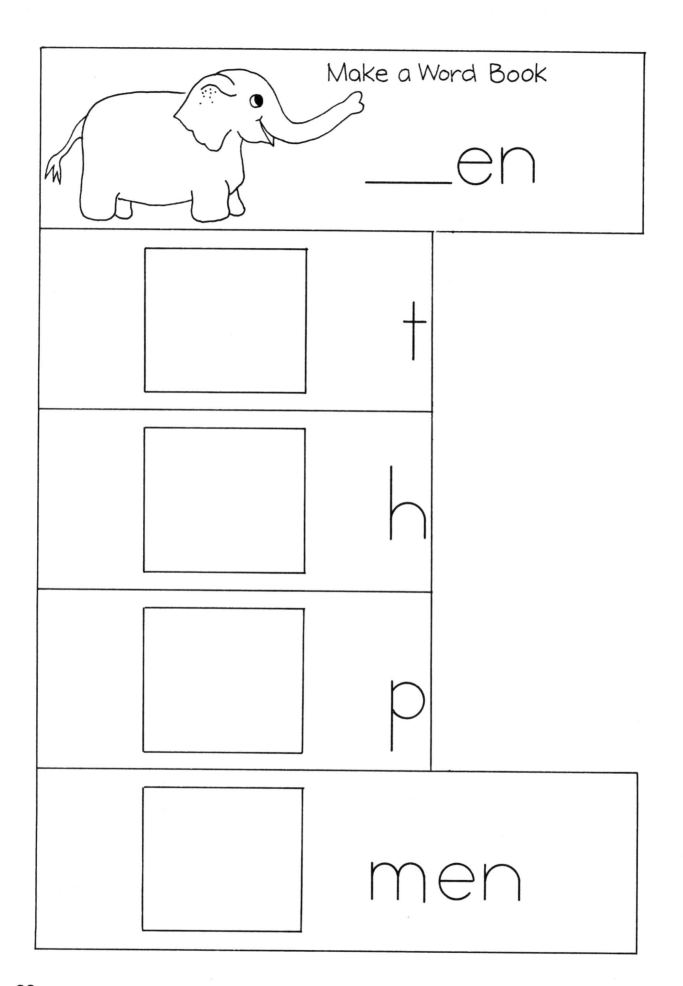

__en

t

h

p

men

Make a Word Book

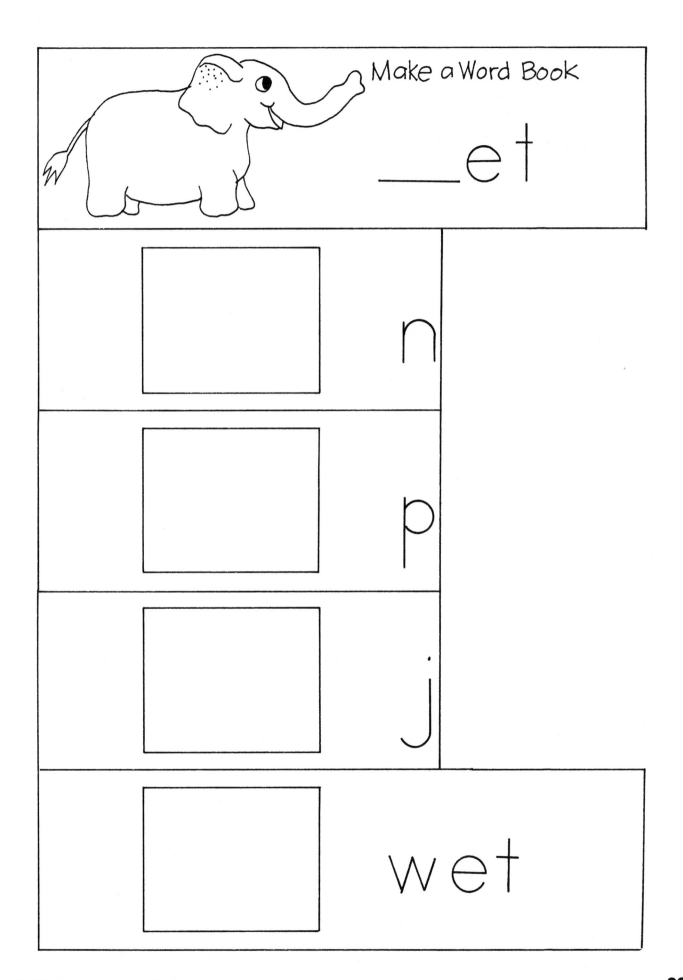

__et

n

p

j

wet

en

- -

et

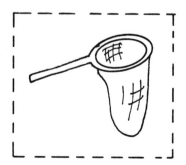 

40

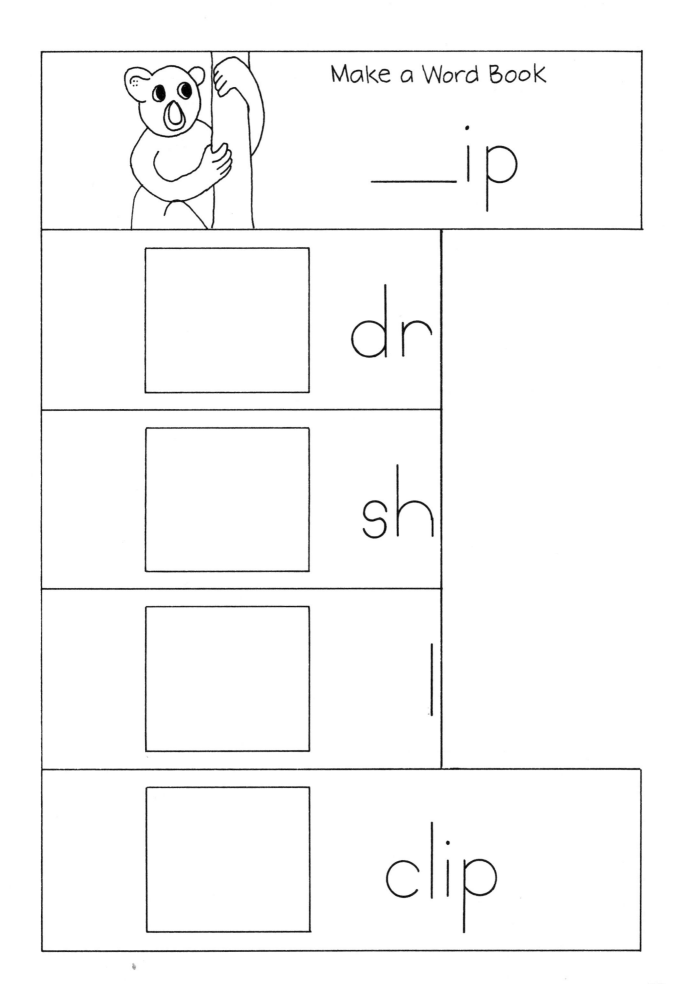

Make a Word Book

__ip

dr

sh

l

clip

41

Make a Word Book

___ing

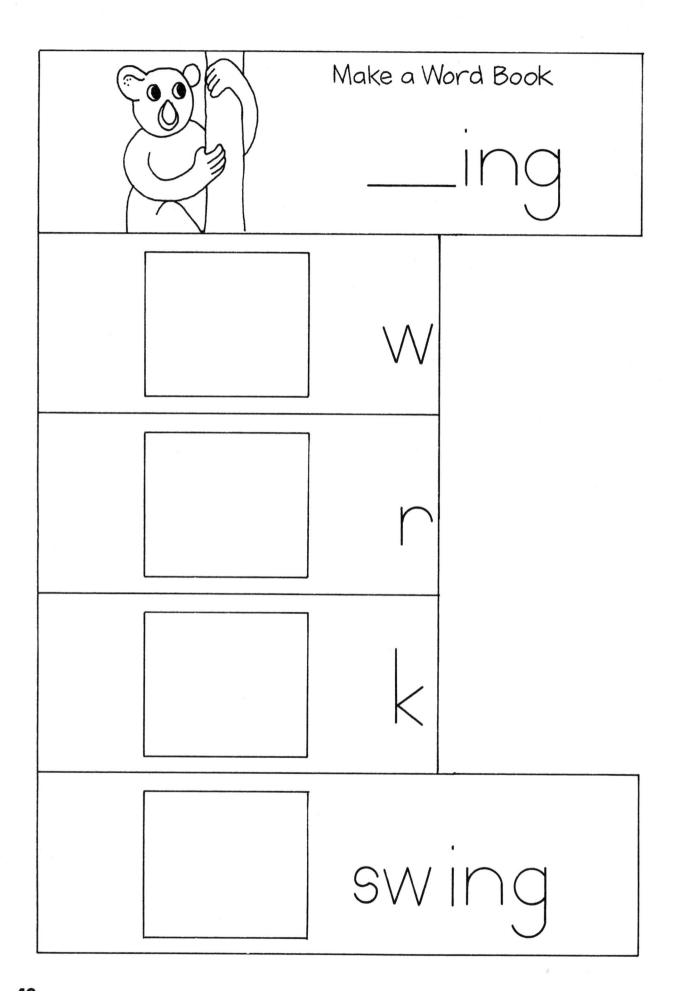

w

r

k

sw ing

ip

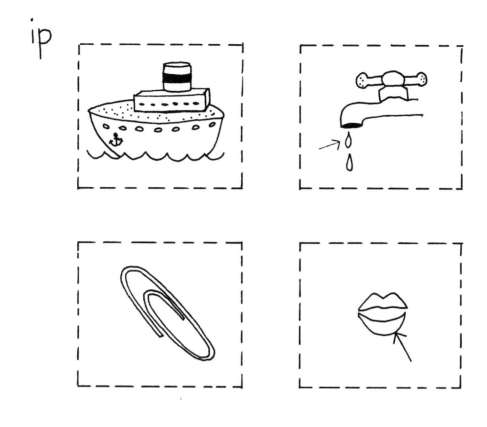

ing

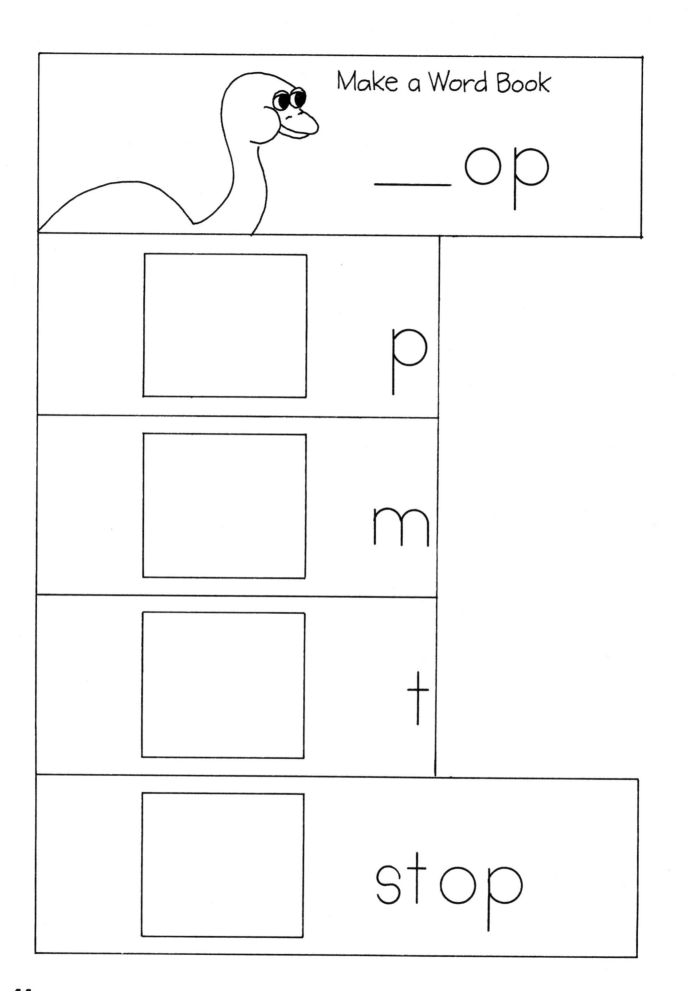

Make a Word Book

__op

p

m

t

stop

Make a Word Book

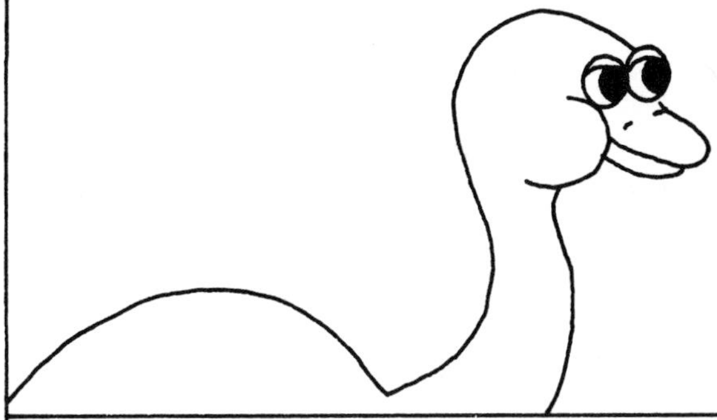

___ock

l

r

cl

s ock

op

ock

46

Make a Word Book

_ug

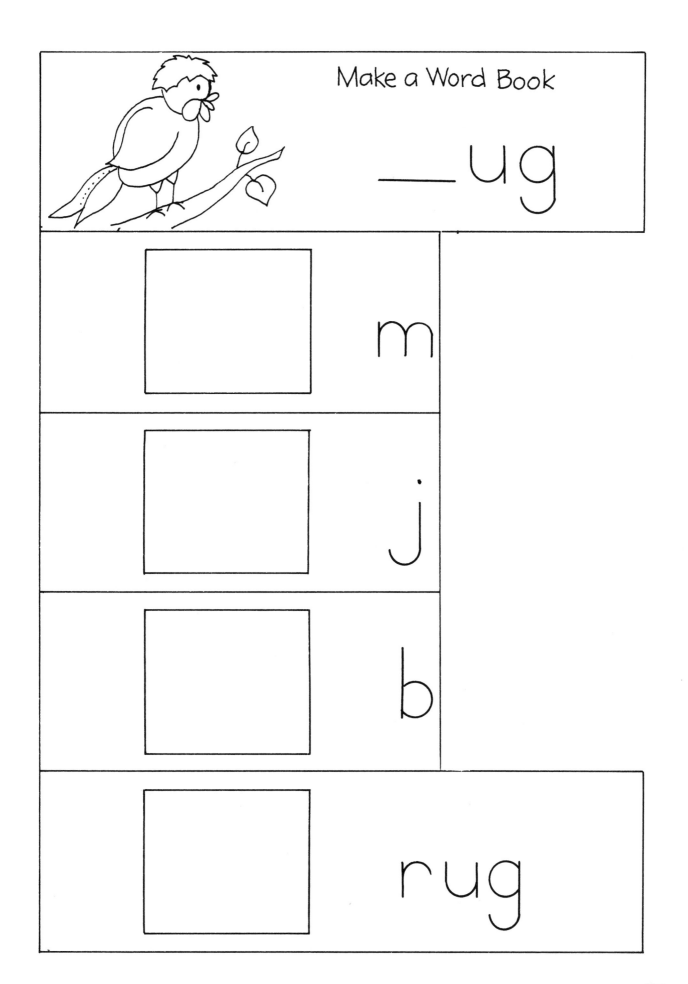

m

j

b

rug

Make a Word Book

___ut

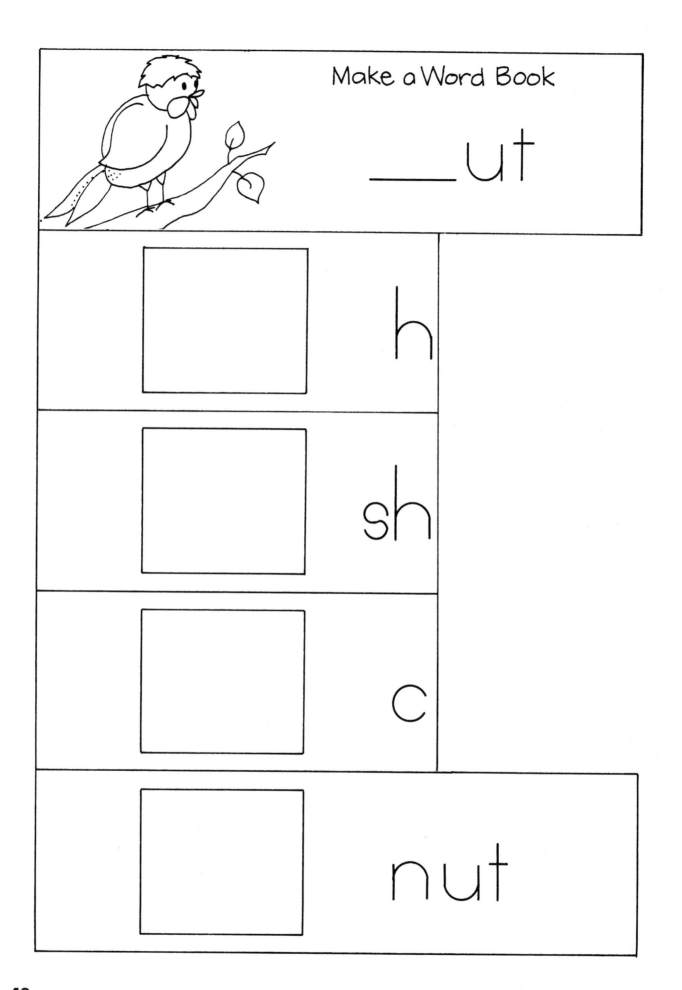

h

sh

c

nut

ug

ut

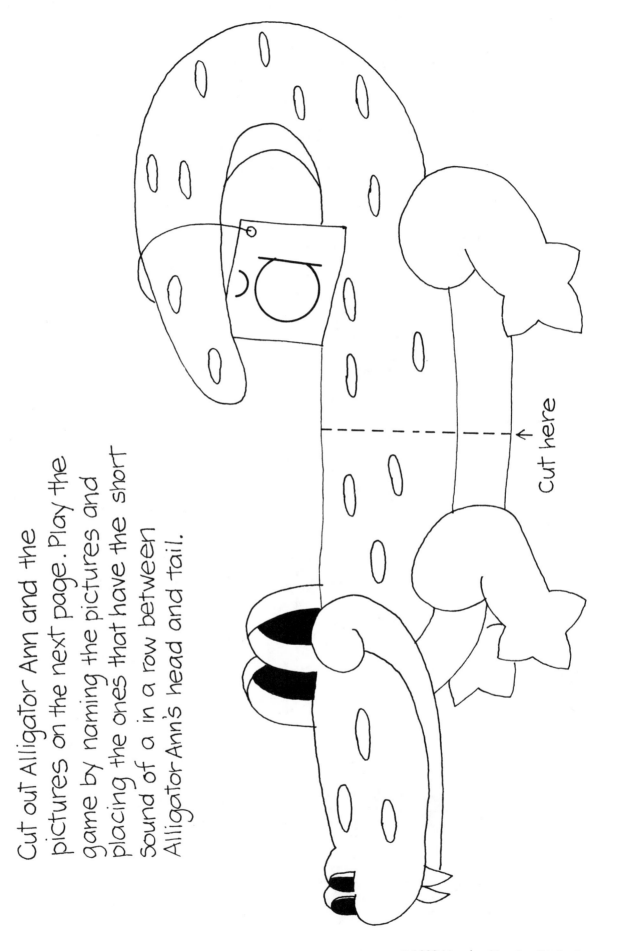

Cut out Alligator Ann and the pictures on the next page. Play the game by naming the pictures and placing the ones that have the short sound of a in a row between Alligator Ann's head and tail.

Cut here

50

ă Alligator Ann's Game

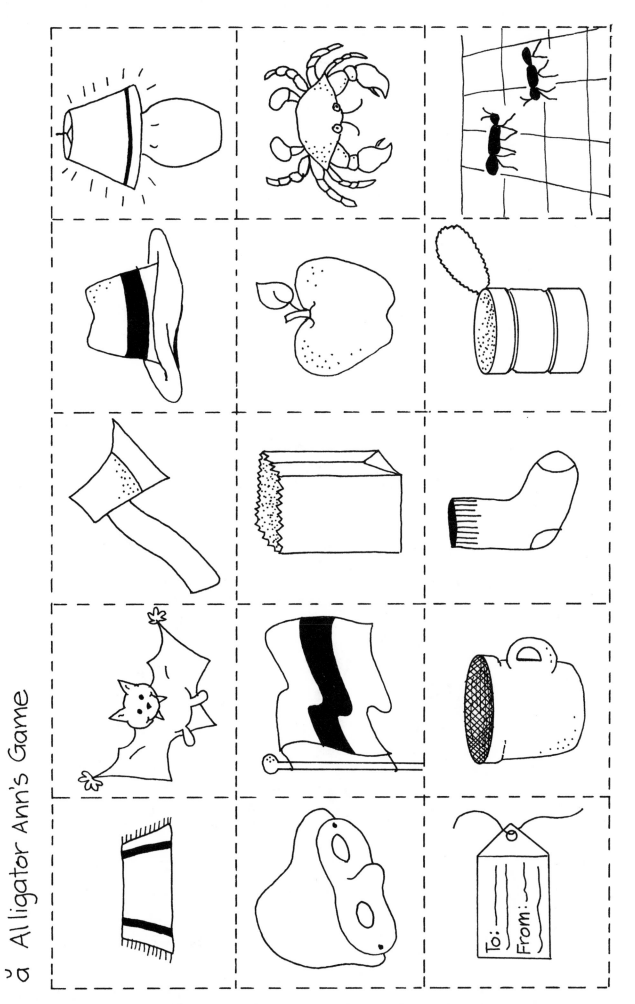

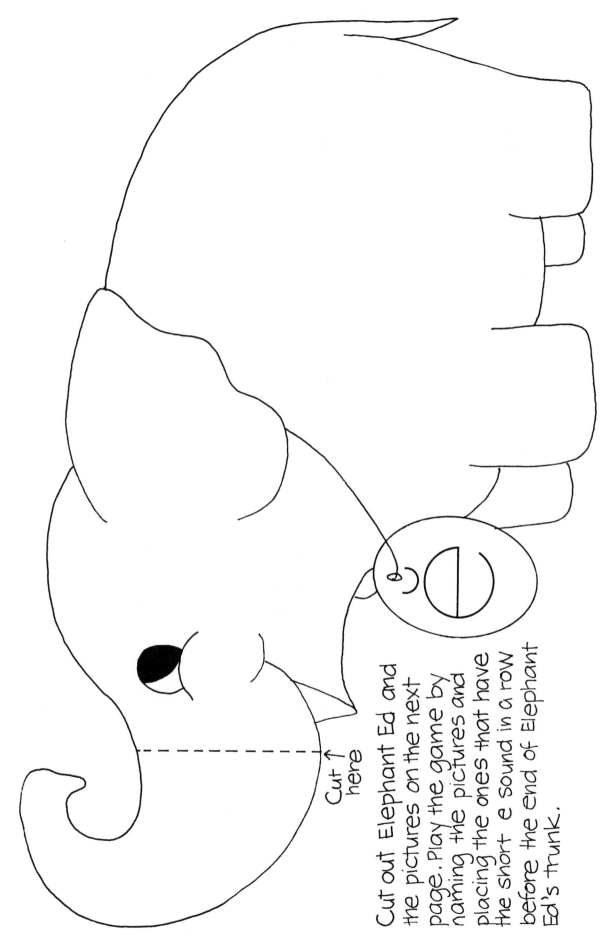

Cut↑ here

Cut out Elephant Ed and the pictures on the next page. Play the game by naming the pictures and placing the ones that have the short e sound in a row before the end of Elephant Ed's trunk.

ĕ Elephant Ed's Game

Cut out Ichabod Indri and the pictures on the next page. Play the game by naming the pictures and placing the ones that have the short i sound in a row to make Ichabod Indri climb higher and higher in the tree.

54

Ichabod Indri's Game

Oliver Ostrich's Game

Cut out Oliver Ostrich and the pictures. Watch Oliver's neck grow by naming the pictures and placing the ones that have the short o sound in a row between his body and his head.

Cut out Umbrella Bird and the pictures on the next page. Play the game by naming the pictures and placing the ones that have the short u sound to make Umbrella Bird's tail grow.

← Cut here

ŭ Umbrella Bird's Game

Alligator Ann

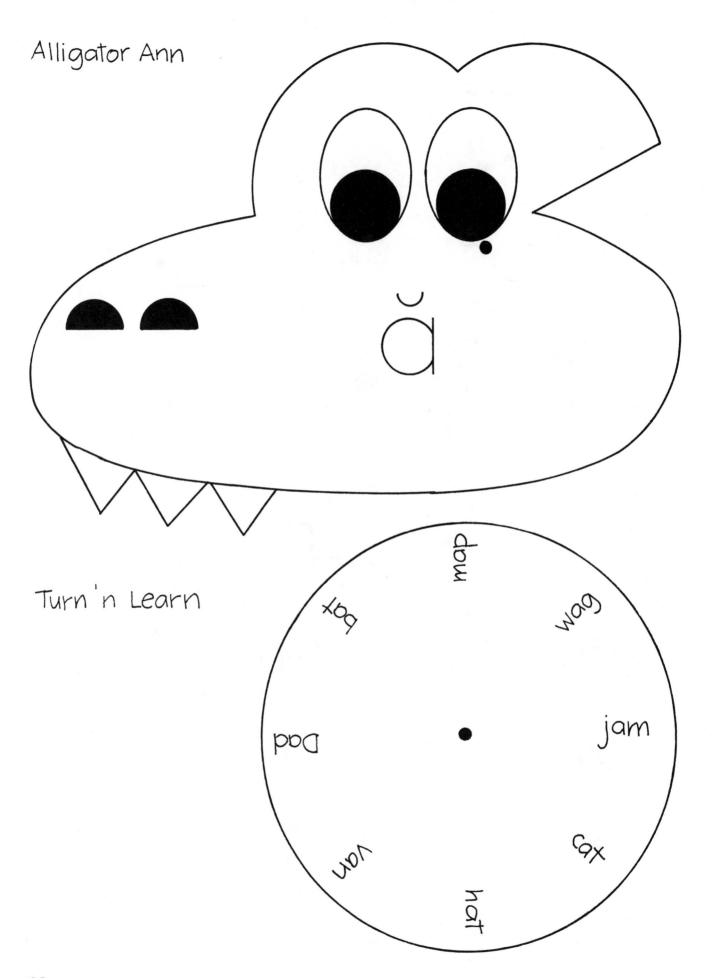

ă

Turn 'n Learn

map
wag
bat
jam
Dad
cat
van
hat

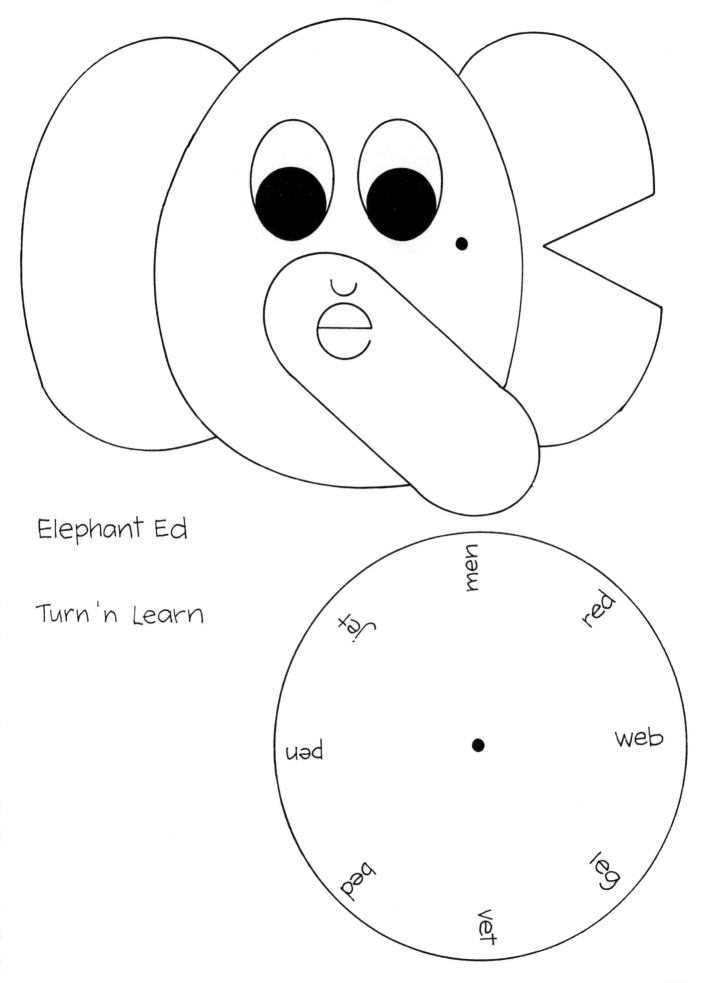

Elephant Ed

Turn 'n Learn

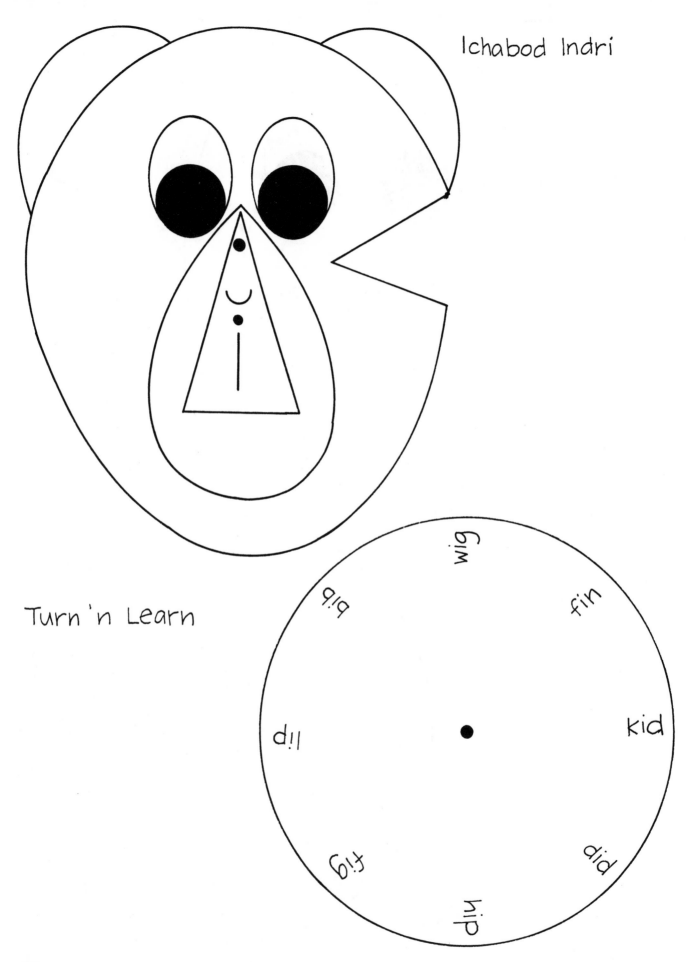

Ichabod Indri

Turn 'n Learn

Oliver Ostrich

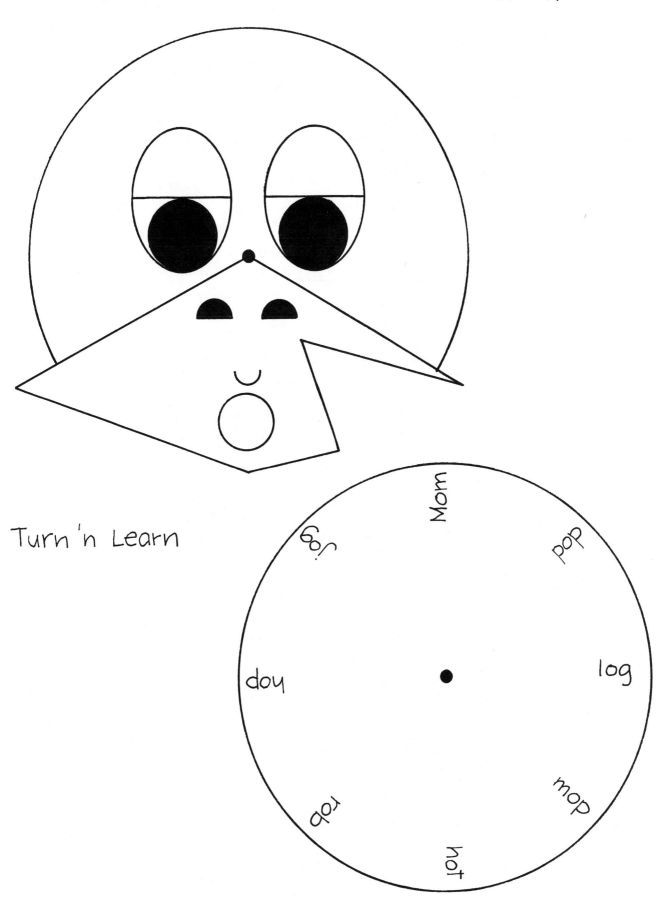

Turn 'n Learn

Mom

pop

jog

log

doy

mop

rob

hot

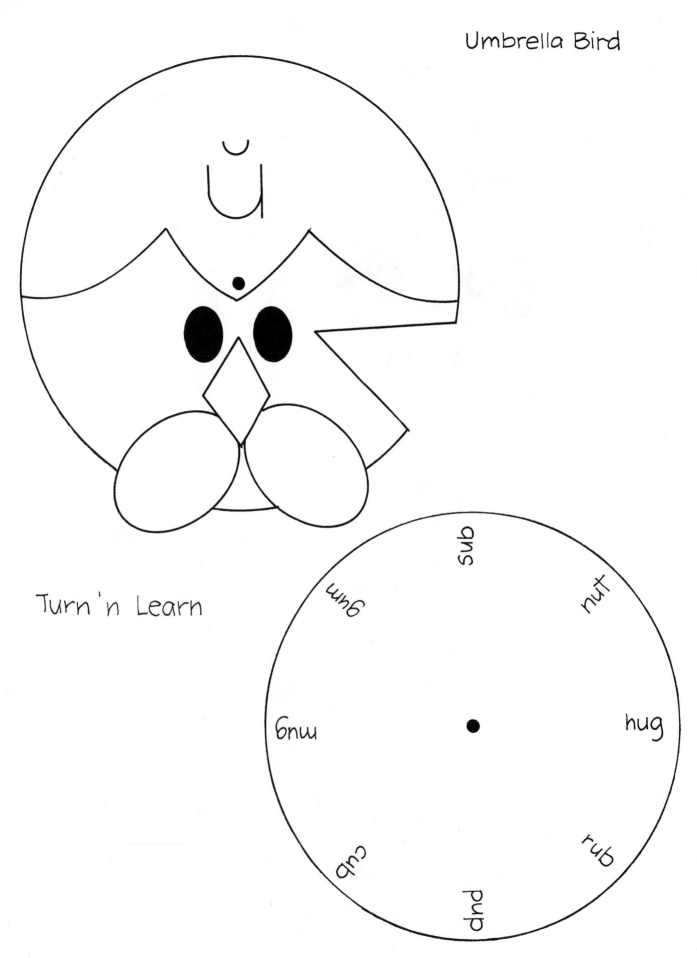

Umbrella Bird

Turn 'n Learn

sub

nut

gum

hug

mug

rub

cub

pup